HERBS FOR KIDNEYS, SKIN AND EYES

Disorders of the kidneys, skin and eyes often originate in emotional problems. The author discusses this important but neglected connection and describes a wide range of herbal remedies for specific complaints.

D1612616

75p

HERBS FOR KIDNEYS, SKIN AND EYES

by
JAAP HUIBERS

Drawings by Gerry Daamen

THORSONS PUBLISHERS LIMITED
Wellingborough, Northamptonshire

Published in Holland as
Kruiden Voor Nieren, Huid En Ogen

© *Uitgeverij Ankh-Hermes bv-Devente 1976*

First published in England 1978

ISBN 0 7225 0453 5

Photoset in Great Britain by
Specialised Offset Services Limited, Liverpool
and printed by
Weatherby Woolnough, Wellingborough, Northamptonshire

CONTENTS

INTRODUCTION

The skin, kidneys and eyes are all capable of feeling. We can feel, obviously, with the skin. It can tell us if something is hot, cold, sharp or blunt. But in what sense can the eyes and kidneys be said to feel?

Clearly, not in any tactile sense: we are not speaking of tangible impressions, but rather of emotional feelings. It is the correlation of the eyes and kidneys with our emotional life that this book deals with, in particular with the kind of person who bottles up their feelings inside. There is a definite link between afflictions of the kidneys and the eyes and the accumulation of unexpressed feelings, particularly of those people we label 'sensitive'.

It is a fact that, in spite of the freedom and latitude of our western society, more and more people seem to suffer from being unable to express their feelings. In fact the expression of genuine and undisguised emotion is regarded with suspicion and embarrassment. For example: many people find it hard to cope with their ageing parents. Old people, once so 'reasonable', often begin to complain – loudly and persistently. But what they are really doing is not moaning: they are not being unreasonable; they are merely showing their feelings, without restraint and without that social decorum that makes it bad form to do so.

Modern society is more prosperous and better organized than ever before, but the price has been the erosion of human contact. We jostle together and crowd into work in a common stream; but though we all enjoy increased wages, better jobs, more possessions and better social facilities than our ancestors, we have lost the art of establishing spontaneous human relationships. This is one reason for the proliferation of alternative cultures amongst the young, who feel exasperated by the way society ignores basic human impulses.

Television seems an apt symbol here. In the past the family, once the day's work was done, had some time to spend in each other's company. But now, the evening meal over, what usually happens is that the television is switched on, destroying any real contact between the members of the family. Discussions, games, a walk, reading together; all belong to the past. Deep down, we barely know each other. Even on holiday people get upset and annoyed if the holiday home does not contain a television set and begin to wonder out loud how they are going to get through the next two weeks without it.

But the denial of deep human contact encourages three things that typify modern society: superficiality, banality and loneliness. Only by awakening a concern for others can these things be overcome, and only by becoming aware of our own feelings can a more humane and more genuinely creative society be established.

This does not mean that we should all give vent to our emotions in a haphazard, uncritical way. We must preserve some balance, if only out of respect for other people. We must learn not to bother ourselves or others with unnecessary outbursts of feeling, but this must be done in the first place by establishing real contact with other people, by talking more with each other, and by expression and understanding.

Finding this vital balance is a necessary task for all of us. To achieve it we must learn to see and feel correctly, discovering what to keep to support a healthy emotional life and what to discard. The latter is a kind of spiritual filtration analogous to the function fulfilled by the kidneys, just as the eyes and the skin are analogous to the way our mind interprets the outside world.

In our search for our vital balance the following words from the *I Ching*, a Chinese book nearly three thousand years old, might well be taken as a guide:

Exultation goes hand-in-hand with love
Success goes hand-in-hand with good morals
What advances goes hand-in-hand with right
Steadfastness goes hand-in-hand with wisdom

Finally, a word about herbs. When a doctor is confronted with a patient complaining of kidney, skin or eye complaints he will not automatically perceive a link with the emotional life. In any case the doctor is a busy man, with a waiting room full of people, and perhaps feels he has no time to delve into the psychological and emotional problems of his patient. And so, with the best intentions, chemical preparations are prescribed the value of which are dubious and whose long-term effects may be positively harmful.

Medicinal herbs, on the other hand, are nature's own products, more suited to the delicate structures of the body. Our skin, for instance, will derive more benefit from a little St John's wort oil than from any chemically prepared product. This will be dealt with in greater detail in later chapters.

CHAPTER ONE

BODY AND SOUL

Sorrow is a truly human phenomenon; everyone grieves at one time or another. Despite this fact, there probably are few of us who have ever stopped to think 'what does sorrow really amount to?' In the first place, we are likely to say that sorrow is something of a nuisance. It is better to have pleasure in one's life. The world has its troubles enough. In order to understand properly the essence of sorrow we must realize that it is something that never comes unaccompanied. Sorrow always has something to do with someone else or something that lies beyond ourselves but with which we still feel involved. Sorrow is, of course, connected with our capacity to form a relationship with things around us. We can become attached to things. This rational aspect of humankind is one of the original principles of humanity. In the biblical story of the creation we read that God, after he had created Adam, said 'Is it not good that the man should be alone'. Like it or not, we all need each other. Man is born for living-together.

History teaches us that the community is often a source of great trouble and conflict. As we have already said in the introduction, man must recognize that his purpose is to seek perfect harmony in his living-together. For many of us, living at a time when disharmony is at a premium, this is no simple task. The important relational aspect of being a human means, amongst other things, that man is dependent on his fellows. Without each other, we simply could not exist, not only in a physical but certainly, also, in a spiritual sense. This makes us vulnerable. The attitudes and reactions of the one impinge on those of the other.

Children these days are taught to close their eyes to the problems they encounter throughout their lives. If they come across any difficulty or set-back, they are fobbed off with the excuse that worse things can and will happen and this sort of talk will encourage them to bottle up their feelings.

When everything gets too much for us we use a safety valve. In the book of Job, we find a splendid example of the emotions–kidney relationship. When Job was abandoned by his friends and everything had been taken away from him, he had to put up with quite a few dents in his feelings. When Job gives vent to his mental state, he says '... he cleaveth my reins asunder and doth not spare' (Job 16, 13). In the book of Proverbs, also, we find one of the many biblical examples of the feelings–kidneys relationship. 'My son, if thine heart be wise, my heart shall rejoice, even mine. Yea, my reins shall rejoice when thy lips speak right things' (Proverbs 23, 15 and 16). Is it not extraordinary to find that our speech and language give clear indications as to the parts of the body concerned with our emotional life?

What, then, are the mechanics of this process? When do disorders really originate? The answer is quite simple: when there is something essentially wrong in man's relational world. Or in other words, when someone has to cope continually with difficulties when trying to create ties with people. I shall now take a closer look at the kidneys, eyes and skin, in each case in relation to our emotional life.

THE KIDNEYS

The kidneys are the organs that filter our blood. We can compare them with a 'purification installation'. The liquid discharged by the kidneys (urine) takes with it many substances that are toxic to the body. In the kidneys, the blood is purified and the waste products are separated from it. As it happens, a relationship appears to exist between our spiritual state and the composition of our blood. If, for example, we have to put up with a lot of trouble, our kidneys will have to work harder since our blood is then more contaminated. If tensions in our emotional life last too long or are too intensive our kidneys are likely to become overworked and if things fail to improve, begin to protest. The following situation may act as an example.

It sometimes happens that women have trouble with their kidneys during the first years of marriage. No one understands why this happens. In a typical situation a woman who has enjoyed good health marries; she has a fine house and her husband has an excellent job and there are no financial worries; but still things are not quite right. What appears to be such a happy situation at first sight may be found to be a real tragedy if we penetrate beneath the surface of the relationship. Before the marriage, marriage was all the woman desired: her entire happiness lay in uniting her life with her fiancé.

Courteousness, amiability, and so on appeared to be the features of the man in question. But once they were married, the husband slowly changed. He seemed in actual fact to be not at all as courteous and affable as she might have indicated before the marriage. The wife feels less attracted to him and deep in her heart, sorry that she ever married him. Before the marriage, her husband played a particular role in order to attract her to him. Once married, the true nature of a person emerges. Women often find themselves tied to someone who is completely different to the man who had courted her.

This is in fact a situation where the kidneys can become the victim of the emotional crisis that slowly unfolds. It is a sorrow of the soul that is difficult to express and, therefore, to resolve. There is no way out for spiritual anguish. However, nature knows no half measures. What cannot be done one way (e.g. by altering the circumstances) will be done in another (e.g. via the body). The cumulation of disharmony within the system must in fact be eased out.

It is therefore of vital concern not to retain the sorrow of your soul too long. Don't bottle it up, but try to free yourself of the disharmony that could make an assault on your body. With all afflictions of the kidneys, you must momentarily ask yourself whether oppressive relationships may exist with others. Examine the world of your relationships and try to introduce balance into it. Introducing balance into our relational world is probably the best medicine for all disorders of the kidneys. If this is not done first of all, recourse to herbs will not bring a lasting cure, since the cause has not been removed.

THE SKIN
Our skin has many functions. The function we are concerned with here is that of releasing humidity. Like our kidneys, our skin is able to excrete 'toxins' from our body. Transpiration is of great importance to man. Once again, there is a relationship between the function of our

skin and the state of our emotions. We see something of this in the way in which we use language, when we say for example 'he broke out in a cold sweat'. The state of our psyche (in this case fear) is the reason why the skin displays an increased discharge of humidity (sweat). In many cases, disorders of the skin are the consequence of a reduced kidney function. The skin takes on the work of the kidneys. It is probable that the relationship between the skin and our emotional life is rather different from that which we discussed with regard to the kidneys. But it is a subtle difference. In both cases, we are concerned with the world of attachments. Afflictions of the kidneys are mainly the consequence of a disturbance in an existing relationship which cannot be broken, even if we wanted it to. With afflictions of the skin, it is mainly a question of the inability to bring about a fully mature relationship. In one way or another, we always seem to rebuff each other, although this is not what we really want. Disorders of the skin that may occur during the years of puberty are not so unexpected, if we follow this line of thought. During puberty, the child is confronted for the first time with the creation of his personal relationships, i.e. without parental participation in any decision he may take. The years of puberty appear to present many children and their parents with communication problems. At that stage, the child does not know whether it should become attached to people and things as child or as adult. It tries to set up adult relationships but finds that he is not yet mature enough to cope with them. As soon as a young person is able to make more or less adult relationships, the spots seem to disappear.

We also find various skin affectations amongst

bachelors who in actual fact would like to have a proper fixed relationship. Acne and eczema are common occurrences in such cases. It is noteworthy also that a woman of thirty to forty years of age will often blame a skin rash on the face. 'Because my face looks this way, no one really wants me' is then the argument put forward. The truth is in fact otherwise. Because no real attachments can be formed (perhaps because our standards are too high or we are too critical in other ways) no harmonious relationship is ever achieved. The anguish of the soul that then results is commonly not adequately discussed, so that the body will react via the places that are analogous to our emotional life. We sometimes hear people speak about 'impure blood' where skin rashes are concerned. All kinds of blood purifiers are tried. Usually, however, without lasting results. You will by now realize why. The blood is in fact impure, but purifying agents will give little or no relief unless the cause is also removed. A pure emotional life will produce pure blood.

Finally, a word about the measurability of our feelings. An apparatus exists with which skin resistance can be measured. It directs a very weak current through the skin and so measures the resistance that the skin offers. It appears that if the emotions of the test subject are aroused or influenced, the skin resistance changes. In America, an apparatus of this kind is used as a 'lie detector', since the state of a person's emotional make-up will change the moment he tells a lie.

THE EYES

Our eyes hold a very special place within the trio dealt with in this book. We are able with our eyes not only to see but also to discharge something – the tear fluid.

In addition to the eye-humidifying function of the tear fluid, it seems further to have a task that is expressed when we cry. We usually cry when we are sad. When everything becomes too much for us, we can burst into tears. We are then no longer able to assimilate the impressions that impinge upon us. Crying is an emergency measure of the body. It is the body's acute detoxification measure. The toxic body juices are expelled with the tear fluid. That crying is an emergency measure of the body is clear from the fact that a child is more likely to cry than an adult. A child is not yet able to fully assimilate the impressions that it gains. A child's spiritual life is more easily harmed than that of an adult. When the child is confronted with things that it cannot understand, it will probably start to cry. By doing so, the child prevents the toxic precipitation of the disharmonious influences that it sometimes experiences from remaining in the body and protects itself against other unpleasant phenomena that might possibly be the result. Unforunately, crying is all too often associated with not being strong. If you are strong, you grit your teeth and hold back your tears. The question that then immediately comes to mind is 'where have the tears got to, then?' Well, that is something we soon discover when confronted with the unpleasant consequences of always being so strong. Eventually, bottled up emotions will find an outlet. If not through tears, then through the skin or, worse, the kidneys. Crying is therefore a very healthy and necessary function. This does not mean that you must always have your tears ready. That is another extreme, which is not harmonious either. When everything has become too much, a little cry seems to offer great relief. We sometimes think 'if only I could cry, then there would be some break in the tension'. This feeling of tension is caused by the cumulation of spiritual toxins that precipitate in the blood. In addition to this detoxifying function of our eyes, it would also appear that seeing is related to our emotional life.

Here, too, our use of language reveals something. When we do not value a relationship with a certain person, we might say 'I can no longer stand the sight of him'. Sometimes, too, of a situation that is not entirely a happy one, we might say 'I don't like the look of it'. Cases are known where sight has improved after a situation that the person concerned 'did not like the look of' was alleviated. Temporary blindness is also sometimes the result of the fact that we can no longer see the way out of a situation in which we may find ourselves. As soon as a change occurs in the situation, the power of sight seems to return, even if not always totally.

Summarizing, we may say that kidneys, skin and eyes are the organs of our body that are in closest sympathy with our emotional lives. There is a form of analogy, as it were, between the two worlds. Both our emotional life and our organs of feeling (kidneys, skin and eyes) are aspects of the same 'original pattern'. Those of you who know something about the laws of astrology or cosmology will realize that the afflictions of the organs dealt with here fall under the cosmic pattern attributed to Venus. The characteristics of this pattern form the basis, as it were, of many phenomena that may occur in analogical form. When studying a natal horoscope, we shall, when assessing the planet Venus, always have to keep an eye on its physical aspects as described in this book.

The metal that has a curative effect on our skin, kidneys and eyes is *copper*. People who have trouble with the world of their attachments should wear copper jewellery. After all, it is through copper that we are all connected to each other (e.g. in the form of the world-embracing telephone cable network, which consists of copper wire).

Do not overload your emotional life and learn to recognize your limits. In all circumstances, avoid bottling up your feelings, particularly of sadness. Make sure that you can unburden your emotional life at the proper time as harmoniously as possible. Give vent to your feelings and never retain disharmonious tendencies in your spiritual life. They can do nothing but harm you.

Retain the feelings that are dear and affectionate in your heart and cherish them so that they contribute to the growth of your whole personality!

CHAPTER TWO

THE CURATIVE POWERS OF LOVING

Although it cannot be obtained from the chemists, love appears to be one of the best medicines that we have to hand. What can hardly, if at all, be achieved with the contents of a medicine bottle seems possible through giving true love. I have already pointed out in the introduction that the world in which we live is so constituted that it is very prone to catching cold. Everything may be beautifully arranged, but where do we stand with the essential intentions of man himself? Fewer and fewer people seem to be really able to love. The reason for this is obvious. Superficiality and self-interest are increasing by leaps and bounds. Our concern for one another diminishes daily. Yet, everyone has need for love, even if sometimes we forget what this really means.

In the previous chapter mention was made of the relationship that exists between our capacity to form attachments and our 'organs of feeling'. A logical consequence is that love will influence these organs, since love is always bound up with man's relational aspect. It really makes little difference whether we form an attachment because we love or whether we love after an attachment has been formed. It is a fact that loving always has something to do with making attachments. The world of human feelings can become unbalanced if it is deprived of love. Love imparts a feeling of protection and we simultaneously discover that someone has respect for and interest in *our* person. Our feelings find a home with the person who loves us. Loving is the great secret to the daily sounding-board that everyone of us needs. Although no one can manage without love, it is of vital importance to those who experience difficulty in their emotional lives.

You will wonder what practical value anything of the above really has. If you already have difficulty in creating relationships, it would seem quite impossible to start loving just like that. Yet, the art of loving can be learned. In the first place, loving must not be confused with being in love. In *essence*, there is no connection between the two. We can, after all, be in love without really loving the person with whom we are in love, and we can in fact love someone without ever having been in love with them. Loving may fall entirely beyond the sphere of the erotic. Loving is universal, it affects all aspects of life where we are really concerned with our deepest being. Once a person who has difficulty in the world of attachments discovers the true essence of loving, he will not find it difficult to give shape to it. The inability to give shape to something is largely due to unfamiliarity with the material to which shape is to be given. As soon as initial contact (through the eyes and skin) has been made, we shall experience a feeling that can perhaps best be described with the words from the book of Proverbs 'Yea, my reins shall rejoice'.

In order really to love something or someone, we must above all proceed with *trust, respect* and *consideration* for each other. How many people honestly feel that they receive sufficient consideration? Consideration may have a negative sound when it is a matter of drawing attention to oneself. However, as soon as we have trust and respect for each other, we shall also have mutual consideration. A little true, loving, attention will have more significance for certain people than to possess a million pounds. The will to give consideration is also a facet of a balanced attachment. Truly to show consideration to a fellow being means making something of our personal feelings visible. This can be called loving. Often, we are not able to love because we dare not give ourselves to something or someone. This inability to give in turn originates from an often unconscious feeling of *vulnerability*. If only we can be sure beforehand that the relationship that we wish to enter into will really come about. Here lurks the heart of all difficulties in forming attachments. We find this balance when, despite many disappointments, we continue to feel, respect and trust in everything we see around us.

In the same way that the kidneys safeguard and promote chemical balance in the blood, really daring to love will safeguard balance in our emotional lives. Disappointments and difficulties with regard to loving can produce imbalances in our emotional lives. If our emotional life becomes overburdened, our sensory organs will have something to say about it.

CONCLUSION
This chapter is perhaps somewhat lacking in medical advice. Yet, it is of fundamental importance since without a real insight into the deeper causes of our complaints we shall not be cured. A true cure must always be achieved on several fronts at once – in the body, the mind and the world around us. Because the situation of our emotional life is so important as regards our kidneys, eyes and skin, a chapter of the present kind had to be written.

CHAPTER THREE

HOW HERBS ARE USED

There are many ways in which herbs may be used. If we dig into the old herbals, we will discover that our ancestors knew far more about herbs that we do nowadays. Some preparatory methods have been lost sight of, or even worse, totally forgotten, partly due to the influence of modern chemical medications. Fortunately, much has also been kept. We shall limit ourselves here to the following possible uses of herbs:

1. use of the fresh herb,
2. use of the dried herb (herbal teas),
3. use of herbal tincture,
4. use of herbal tablets.

THE FRESH HERB

There are some disadvantages in using fresh herbs. First of all, we must have proper knowledge of the various kinds of plants. After all, we must be certain that the plant that we pick is really the herb intended. Many plants are so characteristic that no difficulty will arise. Of some plants there are different varieties. In cases of that kind, the difference is one of nuance. This is the case, for example, with camomile, chervil and the varieties of mint. Always make sure, therefore, that you have got hold of the right plant.

Secondly, a great many plants appear to be polluted in one way or another. Whether through exhaust gases or through artificial fertilizer or weed killers, plant pollution is a very common occurrence these days. Never pick plants by the wayside, in pasture or at the edges of ditches. In nearly every case, these plants are polluted.

Thirdly, we must say that if everyone were to go about the countryside picking medicinal herbs unnecessary damage would no doubt be caused. Although it is done unintentionally, we all too often see people trampling down and picking far more than is really necessary. To pick herbs, more expertise is required than you might think at first. If you bear these points in mind and then set to work with respect for nature, there is of course no reason at all why you should not go about the countryside and discover your own plants that are good for you. Merely tracking down your plant and observing it in its surroundings can have a beneficial effect.

In many cases, the fresh herb is used *externally*. For example, a leaf may be placed on a sore spot or recourse may be made to a herbal plaster. Tea can be made from fresh herbs if you are able to determine the exact quantities. This is not always as simple as it seems since fresh herb has a much stronger effect than the dried variety. In practice, dried herbs are the more commonly used since plants of a particular herb are, of course, not always available.

DRIED HERBS
To dry herbs that you have picked yourself they should be placed on clean paper (*not* on newspaper, since the ink contains lead) in a moderately warm well-aired place (never in direct sunlight). When the herb is dry – after a week or so, depending on circumstances – it can be cut into fine pieces (preferably with a silver knife) and kept in glass jars with a good seal.

Nowadays, nearly all herbs can be bought in

the dry form from a chemist or health store. However, always look carefully at the quality of the herb. If a herb is kept for more than a year it loses much of its properties.

MAKING HERBAL TEA

Never use a metal teapot since this can give rise to changes in the properties of the herb. Add a heaped dessertspoonful of herbs (either of a specific herb or of a herbal mixture) to about half a litre of water (three teacups). Pour a half litre of boiling water on the herbs, let it stand for some ten to fifteen minutes, and then sieve the mixture. If kept in a cool place, the tea, less its tea leaves, can be kept for a day. In this way, you can make tea in the early morning to last the whole day.

The first cup should be drunk warm. Unless stated otherwise, a cup of herbal tea may be taken three times a day, about ten to fifteen minutes before meal times. When a herbal mixture is composed of dried herbs, the proportions can best be determined by dessertspoonsful of the herb. The various herbals usually indicate so many 'parts' of this and so many of that. For 'parts' read dessertspoonsful.

HERBAL TINCTURE

Making tinctures yourself is no easy task. Not all tinctures have the same percentage of alcohol. If, however, you really want to experiment yourself, you should preferably choose brandy as the alcoholic base. Like dried herbs, tinctures can also now be bought at chemists and health stores. Dosages will depend chiefly on the herb concerned and on the individual nature of the person taking the herb. As regards quantity, never be too thrifty when using herbal tinctures. One droplet more or less will not make that much difference. You must remember, though, that quantity does not always provide quality! Often, we can see more results from using two to three drops a time than when fifteen or twenty drops are taken. We shall deal with this matter further in the chapter on homoeopathy.

HERBAL TABLETS
These are tablets pressed from the dried herb. Some herbs cannot take alcohol so that tincture cannot be prepared from them. In some cases, too, the effect of herbal tablets appears to be greater than that of the tincture of the herb.

OTHER WAYS OF USING HERBS
The effect of herbs is fundamentally different from that of allopathic medicaments. It will be clear from the previous chapters that physical imbalance is part of a much greater pattern. Imbalance of the body will manifest itself analogously in other fields. A cure only becomes a true cure when the original pattern that has been upset and which lies at the root of the symptoms is harmonized. We should, therefore, not attempt to combat a sickness with just one substance that has a certain effect at one point in the body (i.e., the principle of the active component of the substances), but with a complete pattern of something that has a harmonizing effect on our system as a whole. What concerns us in fact is not only the specific substances in the plant that bring about a cure. It is the overall pattern of the plant itself which has a curative effect on our system. Alas, slowly but surely, we have come to forget the true nature and significance of our plants. We no longer recognize in the plant the essence of the

greater pattern of which the plant is a reflection. If, however, we delve more deeply into the nomenclature we find countless indications concerning the 'essence' of the plant. After all, plants have not acquired their names at random. In past times, people knew that given names had to reveal something of the essence of things. This applied not only to plants, but also to man and animal. Many plant names point to a certain effect on a specific use, e.g. *sani*cle, *life*root, eyebright, *lady*'s mantle, *wound*wort and many others. This nomenclature is quite certainly not due to chance.

A plant can therefore represent a pattern that fits with the symptoms that are present within you at any particular moment. In addition to internal use of the appropriate herb, merely wearing a spray of the herb can have a harmonizing effect. In this way, you always carry the harmonizing pattern with you. The same applies to the appropriate stone and the associated metal. Why should we not carry with us a leaf of the herb or a piece of a metal which we have come to love because we are convinced that it has a good effect on our system? Don't we often carry with us a photo of the person whom we love and who we are sure has a harmonizing effect on us?

For the casually thinking person, this may all seem rather odd. Always remember that much criticism is a result of ignorance. Never, therefore, try and convince another that you are right. This is a waste of time. Remain yourself and allow the richness of the balance growing within you to radiate. As soon as you begin to radiate truth, any attempt to supply proof will be put in the shade.

Once you have learned to gain insight into

this reality, you will discover that there are many ways of using herbs beyond the more functional ones. However, this requires a way of thinking that does not result from the materialistic causal pattern. It demands insight. Perhaps, discovery of the essence of the plant will become a foundation for your further spiritual growth.

CHAPTER FOUR

HERBAL REMEDIES

GOLDEN ROD
(Solidago virga aurea)

The Golden Rod is one of the best of the kidney herbs. It is a herb that fits perfectly with the sensitive kind of person (the Venus type). In ancient times, *Solidago* was already being used for healing wounds (the 'wounds of the soul' are analogous). Its name also reflects something of this quality.

Solidago is derived from *solidare*, which means to make sound. The herb is particularly apt for the kind of person who feels himself caught up within an existing relationship which he would like to break off. The circumstances, however, are such that it is easier said than done. As a result, the emotions have a great

Golden Rod
(Solidago virga aurea)

deal to put up with.

If we are mentally no longer able to cope, it is the kidneys that then seem to bear the brunt. In such cases, *Solidago* is a herb without equal. It stimulates the kidneys and draws water off. The latter is of enormous importance. In the ancient science of the elements, *water* is analogous to *feeling*. We often find dropsical swelling occurring with people who contain their feelings too much. Since their feelings can find no way out, water is also retained in the body. *Solidago* helps us to cross over a threshold. It strengthens the operation of our kidneys and so brings balance into the world of our feelings. However, always accompany *Solidago* with a search for solutions both in our psyche and in our circumstances. Only then will lasting results be obtained. *Solidago* is a cleansing herb. It accordingly also helps with the headache that arises just before and during menstruation. For headache, ten to fifteen drops of *Solidago* tincture should be taken once or twice a day.

Ten drops of Solidago tincture may be taken three to four times a day over an extended period for any kind of kidney complaint. A cup of golden rod tea may also be drunk three times daily. Use one dessertspoonful of dried herb to half a litre of water. Depending on the nature of the complaint, golden rod can be excellently combined with other herbs.

REST-HARROW
(Ononis spinosa)

Although doctors of whatever kind make no distinction between the various ways of retaining liquid, it is generally recognized that this may differ in nature, particularly as regards the true cause. The retention of liquid with Solidago, for example, is quite different in

Rest Harrow
(Ononis spinosa)

character than with Rest-Harrow. To determine which substance we should use in order to 'work' liquid out of the body, we must first give some thought to the background of 'liquid-retention'. The background of the *Solidago*-type is to be caught up in a specific attachment whereby the feelings rebel without there being any way out. Not only our feelings but also our kidneys become overcharged. The *Ononis*-type is not caught up in a specific relationship but keeps his feelings to himself too much by nature. The *Ononis*-type is afraid of expressing himself. We know how vulnerable we are if we wear out hearts on our sleeves. This kind of person will also find it rather strange to talk to someone else about their personal feelings. It is also a characteristic of the type to be rather prudish in their daily circumstances. Such people will quickly run off with a squeal if, for example, someone they know quite well suddenly comes in while they are not fully dressed. One consequence of this inclination is imperfect cleansing. An accumulation of uric acid and fouling of the bowels occurs in the body.

If you recognize yourself as of the above type, recourse to Rest-Harrow will help a great deal. Instead of hygroton (the action of this substance is based on the expulsion of salts, so that large quantities of much needed potassium also leave the body) one could do better to try *Ononis* tincture or tea. According to the situation, ten to fifteen drops of the tincture can be taken three to four times daily.

The tea, made of the dried herb, may, if desired, be combined with other liquid-expelling herbs such as Meadowsweet, Birch leaf, Strawberry leaf and Stinging Nettle. However, never combine Rest-Harrow with Golden Rod since owing to the types of person for which they are suitable they cannot be reconciled.

Also attack the causes. As an exercise in self-expression, one night, for example, write something about one's feelings on the back of a roll of wallpaper. This section of paper can then be stuck to the wall. In this way, we have got rid of our feelings but essentially still have them with us and no one can see it! This may be regarded as a kind of exercise in learning to express our feelings. Try it!

STINGING NETTLE
(Urtica dioica and Urtica urens)

In addition to the value of the stinging nettle as a spring vegetable, it has another highly characteristic property. In earlier times, the fibre of the stinging nettle was used to make nettle muslin. In his *Botanical Lexicon of the*

Stinging Nettle
(*Urtica dioica*)

Netherlands, H. Kleijn repeats the following traditional tale about the stinging nettle and the muslin made from it.

A wicked guardian would not give his ward his permission to marry until she had herself spun her wedding dress from a weed growing by the wayside – the stinging nettle. She went to her room and prayed to God for help. Exhausted, she feel asleep. She then dreamt that she was taken by two angels to the stinging nettle. They informed the girl that she could pick the plants as long as the dew was still wet on them and showed her how the fibres in the stalks could be spun into thread and into muslin. She was then able to use the muslin to prepare her wedding dress. She set to work the next day and when the dress was ready, her guardian suddenly died and she was able to wed.

As is the case with every folk tale, this is very much more than just a story. We can explain it in the following way.

The wicked guardian is a symbol of people with whom we have empty and essentially valueless relationships. We can see relationships of this kind about us every day. These are the relationships that must be proved by material means. In fact, the guardian also made a material demand. If we are caught in this material pattern, we shall experience little spiritual growth and so progress little further in life. However, as soon as we are able to subject the material aspect of a relationship to spiritual consciousness (the wedding in the story), the dominance of the material (the guardian) will cease to exist. The path that we must take in such cases is very much a thorny one. It can also be compared with the transition that everyone has to experience during the years of puberty. We break loose from a more or less imposed relationship with the parental home and try to stand on our own two feet. It is during this period that we first become aware of spiritual values. At such a time, the body has much to put up with. Our feelings, in particular, may become overwhelmed by what we discover in the field of the spirit. The physical phenomena are all too well known – skin affectations of all kinds.

The nettle of the nettle rash is the appropriate herb in such cases. It helps us with the transfer from the childhood phase to adulthood. The fibres are a symbol of our relationships. After all, it is during the years of puberty that we learn to form relationships. These are then no longer child to adult, but adult to adult.

The stinging nettle helps in all cases where our feelings become engulfed by the consequences of a change of phase. Each change of phase in our life means a change in our physical make up. As a result we draw other persons towards us so that we have to enter new relationships. Our emotional life has to assimilate all these new impressions.

Use the stinging nettle for skin rash where this is the result of the pattern described above. Preferably use tea of the dried herb. A cup three or four times a day removes the water and cleans the blood.

It is a well known fact that young people may become listless during the years of puberty. Unconsciously, they dare not as yet face up to the new situation. The stinging nettle instils power of action, since the plant entirely meets the situation in which one finds oneself in such cases.

Teach your children to be careful with this plant and not to see it chiefly as an annoying weed. The time may come when they need it. The large quantities in which this plant occurs may almost be regarded as symbolic. After all, every child will be confronted with the transition from the childhood phase to adulthood. Let us try and understand the instructions that nature itself gives us and to follow them with gratitude. Perhaps the annoying stinging nettle may incline us to yet deeper thought!

CAMOMILE
(Matricaria chamomilla)

The Camomile is a polychrest (a substance with a highly versatile action) amongst herbs. It is regarded as a supplement to the more specifically acting herbs for practically all affectations of the body. The Camomile acts particularly on our nervous system, especially where our emotional life is concerned.

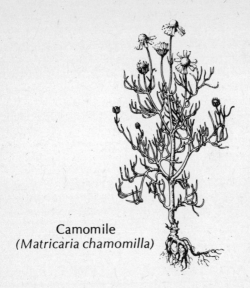

Camomile
(Matricaria chamomilla)

As a herb it is suitable for persons who can never find a proper place for their feelings. Virtually no one is prepared to listen to them. The effect of the Camomile is strongly anti-spasmodic. Spasm is, after all, the consequence of a tense situation. If we can never find a ready ear anywhere, we become frustrated and, consequently, crabbed in our ways and means.

Most affectations of the kidneys are partly the result of a disturbed relationship. This can also lead to tension, both physical and mental. When our experience of the world of attachments has proved so intensively disappointing that we no longer dare face our fellows with an open mind. This crabbed attitude can prove a hindrance to entering new relationships. And in this way we end up in a vicious circle.

In addition to the herbs with a specific action on the kidneys, skin and eyes, the Camomile can be used to achieve a favourable influence on spiritual balance. To five parts of other herbs always add two parts of camomile where a situation exists of the kind described above. Camomile tincture can also be used. The best results are achieved by using the camomile in a homoeopathic solution. For this, see the chapter on homoeopathy.

The chief action of Camomile is therefore *anti-spasmodic*.

CELERY
(*Apium graveolens*)

PARSLEY
(*Petroselium sativum*)

Both celery and parsley can be used to make a delicious soup, either on their own or together. If we set up our own herb garden, parsley and

Celery
(*Apium graveolens*)

celery are some of the first herbs to be planted. These two herbs are not only very tasty, but also highly medicinal and therefore very healthy. Dodoneus, in his *Herbal* writes the following about parsley.

'The roots of these parsleys sieved in water and drunk open the occlusion of the liver, of the kidneys and of all the internal parts; and causes the urine to shed; and the stone and gravel to rise and depart'.

Dodoneus finally says about this herb, 'The leaves of these parsleys mixed with bread cure the red and swollen eyes'.

Celery expels water and is a good specific for kidney stones. A handful of the fresh herb can be allowed to draw in a litre of water for a quarter of an hour (do not boil). This quantity may be drunk gradually throughout the day. Parsley, further, has a strong uric acid expelling effect (to be used particularly for rheumatic and renal patients).

Sensitive persons would do well to take some of the fresh herb daily during the spring and summer. This can prevent disorders of the kidneys and eyes, in view of the herb's fluid-dispelling action. Accumulations of fluid in the body are an 'accumulation of feelings'.

For afflictions of the eye and kidney stone, recourse may be made to parsley tincture over an extended period. Fifteen drops three times a day half an hour before meals.

EYEBRIGHT
(Euphrasia officinalis)

An old medicinal herb which, as the name indicates, is used for conditions of the eye. In addition to their looking function, our eyes always seem to be associated with other parts of the body. According to an old saying, the eyes

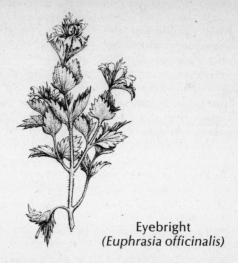

Eyebright
(Euphrasia officinalis)

are the mirrors of the soul. Luke 11, 34 says the following about our eyes: 'The light of the body is the eye: therefore when thine eye is single, thy whole body also is full of light; but when thine eye is evil, the body also is full of darkness.' The eyes are, as it were, 'the barometers of the soul'.

We can learn much about the condition of our emotional life from our eyes. As has already been explained in the earlier chapters, complaints of the eye are directly connected with disorders of our emotional lives. When we can 'no longer see what to do', our eyes appear to react analogously. The power of sight is reduced. As a result of our seeing less, spiritually as well as physically, we become depressed and downhearted. After all, if we see less, we have less chance of making contact with the world about us. The secret of Eyebright is to be found in the meaning of the Latin name

Euphrasia. This name is derived from the Greek verb *euphraino*, which means to make happy. This herb has been originally named according to its side-effects. When the eye was cured, the soul appeared gladdened. In other words, when the eye was purified, the body appeared 'enlightened'. There is in fact no organ in our body so closely concerned with the revelational aspect in man as our eyes. Even the English name tells us something about its action: *brightening* the world of our feelings by curing the *eyes*. With eye complaints of any kind, resort may also be made to tincture of this herb: fifteen drops three times a day. With inflamed eyes, an eye-wash can be made from boiled water to which a few drops of the tincture have been added. Make sure that the liquid contains no impurities. It may be used for rinsing the eyes several times a day. This herb can also be applied externally.

Remember, in particular, that with this herb 'a merry heart doeth good like medicine: but a broken spirit drieth the bones' (Proverbs 17, 22).

LEOPARD'S BANE
(Arnica montana)

Now and again, we find a certain type of eczema occurring as a result of tension in our emotional lives. The nature of these tensions may be described as a result of the breaking-up of a close relationship that leaves us both spiritually and socially dejected. What we considered to be firmly built has collapsed and we are suddenly alone in the world; at least that is how we feel at the time. In many cases, the will to start on anything new no longer exists. If such a situation continues, our skin may be affected. Our feelings cannot find an outlet in the normal way and we are no longer able to

Leopard's Bane
(*Arnica montana*)

build up new relationships. As a result, the
kidney function is impaired and the blood is
imperfectly cleansed. Yet, the impurities must
go somewhere. This is when the skin breaks
open and toxins are released. That is where
Leopard's bane helps.

The skin can be bathed with dilute arnica
tincture (twenty drops in a cup of lukewarm
water) and the herb can also be taken internally.
For internal use, the homoeopathic dilution
should be adopted (see chapter 5). Arnica helps
us over the feelings of dejection. It reinstates
the skin with its regenerative powers and so
strengthens our nervous system.

STAGSHORN CLUBMOSS
(Lycopodium clavatum)

This very rare plant is suitable for young children and old people. Many old people end up spending the 'twilight of their years' in an old peoples home. Though from the social point of view, they are excellent institutions, it does happen from time to time that elderly people have little chance of giving their emotional life a balanced shape once they have arrived in an old peoples home. The nature of the circumstances is such that they lose their own individuality. In some cases, they are unable to cope with the overwhelming kindness shown by the staff. Many old people experience such kindness as rather demoralizing. They feel they are being treated like children, as if the experience of a life-time that they have gained is swept from the table in on go. There are many elderly people who enjoy entertaining the younger generation with their experiences. Old people *can* in fact be very

Stagshorn Clubmoss
(Lycopodium clavatum)

wise people. Once they are in the home, it would seem there is little need for Mr X's wisdom.

This inability to sort out their emotional life takes its revenge. An evil commonly occurring is sluggishness of the kidneys. Unfortunately, when this happens, a diuretic of some form or another is almost always prescribed. But as already stated in connection with the Rest-Harrow, these diuretics ensure that a great deal of salt, but also of potassium, leaves the body. In astrological terms, salt belongs to Mercury. Too little salt produces apathy. We become drowsy and unable to think. In actual fact, therefore, diuretics rob people of their powers of thought!

The Stagshorn Clubmoss appears to act particularly well on the liver and kidneys. It strengthens the ego and we can again cope with the circumstances in which we find ourselves. The use of Stagshorn Clubmoss and *Ononis* (or possibly Golden Rod, depending on the type of person) can help to alleviate much misery amongst elderly people. The Clubmoss is almost always used in a homoeopathic solution (see chapter 5).

Summarizing, we may say that Stagshorn Clubmoss (*Lycopodium*) is a medicinal herb for young children and older people who have difficulties with their emotional lives as a result of predominating circumstances. Like Camomile, *Lycopodium* can support more organically directed therapy.

BLACKTHORN
(*Prunus spinosa*)

The blackthorn has an excellent blood-cleansing action. Petrus Nylandt, in his *Herbal* of 1682, writes as follows about the blackthorn: 'The flowers make the stomach mild and purify

Blackthorn
(*Prunus spinosa*)

the kidneys'. This herb is useful for the quick-tempered type of person who has trouble with the kidneys. With people of this type, it seems that pent-up feelings must be forcefully expelled. So violently, even, that the kidneys are damaged and bleeding may result. Like all representatives of the *Rosaceae* family, this herb, too, has an astringent action, which can be very useful where bleeding is concerned. The herb may also be used for bleeding of the urinary tract resulting from damage through kidney stones. Tea may be made of the leaf and flowers. In many cases, the tincture is applied; ten drops two to four times a day.

The blackthorn has a strong regulatory effect on our whole metabolism. The tincture is therefore sometimes used for fatty degeneration.

Blackthorn may be alternated with *Tormentilla* for bleeding of the kidneys.

DYER'S MADDER
(*Rubia tinctorum*)

Petrus Nylandt describes the plant in the book we have already referred to. He says about it, 'For constipation of the liver, spleen and kidneys: take of the root two parts; sieve it in a half pint each of wine and water until a third part has boiled away; when passed through the sieve, let one small rummer be taken twice a day'.

With ancient writers, constipation generally means that the function of the organ concerned is impeded by stone or growths, and this plant is especially recommended for kidney stone. Accompany the use of *Rubia* tablets with *Solidago* tea, since this is a hydrogogue.

The Rubia cure takes the following lines. One packet of polygorubia (combination of *Rubia*

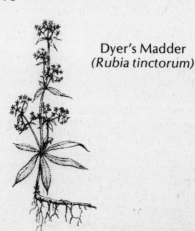

Dyer's Madder
(*Rubia tinctorum*)

tinctorum with Knotgrass) tablets is taken. While taking them, the intake of liquids should be cut down. When the packet is finished, stop for one week, during which a great deal of liquid is taken (including a large quantity of Golden Rod tea). Then, one further packet of tablets is taken. On completing this, too, a great deal must be drunk. In many cases, the stones appear slowly to dissolve. The cure should be repeated once every three months.

BLOSSOM OF THE SMALL-LEAVED LIME
(Tilia cordata)

We could not ask for more on a warm summer evening than to sit beneath the leafy cover of the majestic Lime. Tired from the heat and with no further desire to move, we find from the Lime the necessary rest and coolness. Lime blossom has been used for

Lime
(*Tilia cordata*)

centuries as a diaphoretic herb. When stricken
with 'flu or a heavy cold accompanied by fever,
a cup of Lime blossom tea can be taken with
great success, particularly when transpiration is
difficult. A sip of tea now and again stimulates
the sweat glands and so produces the required
cooling. The Lime is good for the highly
sensitive type, for the person who is open, as it
were, to all knocks given out by life. Frequently,
such people take a long time to assimilate the
impressions they have absorbed. In the Lime
blossom type, feelings cumulate particularly in
the legs and feet and in the head. In the legs
and feet this is expressed as damp swellings, in
the head as dizziness and even epileptic-type
states. For swollen legs, Petrus Nylandt gives the
following recipe. 'Take the leaves of the Lime,
as much as may be required; boil them in water
to a paste and spread it over the swollen legs.'
For giddiness, the following recipe can do good
service: 'Use the distilled water of the Linden
blossom and a conserve prepared of the same
flowers.'

Summarizing, tea from the leaves or blossom
of the Lime can relieve puffy feet and legs. A
compress may also be made of Lime leaf paste.
Lime blossom has a highly cleansing action and
stimulates the metabolism. Lime blossom may
be excellently combined with *Solidago* and the
common Balm. A cup of this tea three times a
day is a good specific for all kinds of dropsical
swelling, particularly for the forms that are
manifested in the lower parts of the body.

BALM
(Melissa officinalis)

If we seek comfort in the plant world, there is
no better herb than Balm. It is a herb for people
who can no longer cope with their ailments or

spiritual life and who are overwhelmed by disharmonious impressions of people. The Latin name is based on honey. Sweetness is something that brings comfort. Just think of all those mothers who haven't the time or the inclination really to comfort their child and who give them sweets to make them feel better. Here, sweetness (alas) replaces motherly love. What *Lycopodium* is for young children and old people, Balm is for those people between the two extremes. Kidney, eye and skin ailments can be avoided if the life of the emotions is duly regulated by using Balm. It harmonizes the emotional life of people who have had to assimilate many dents on their feelings and who are really no longer able to put up with them. A hard personality will certainly have no need for Balm. It is more applicable to the good-natured, caring type who is really not quite at one with

Balm
(*Melissa officinalis*)

hard reality, of the kind that occurs in our
society.

The type described above would do well to
use ten to fifteen drops of Balm tincture two to
three times daily. It is easy to decide for yourself
when it is necessary and in what measure. A
lovely cooling tea may be made from the fresh
herb in the summer. Four to five leaves of the
fresh herb are sufficient for two cups of tea.

Balm is also an excellent remedy for reducing
blood pressure, particularly when the high
pressure is due to reduced kidney function.

CHAPTER FIVE

SOME HOMOEOPATHIC REMEDIES

The principles of homoeopathic medicine are to some extent different from those of herbal healing. With the latter approach, the undiluted form of plants is used. In the case of a tincture, we then refer to the 'simple' tincture. This is indicated by the sign Ø. The principles of homoeopathic medicine are based on the application of substances in special dilute forms. The principles were developed by the famous German physician Samuel Hahnemann (1755-1843). He discovered that certain substances (plants, minerals, metals and the like) produce symptoms which can be cured by applying the same substance highly diluted. He summarized this principle in his well-known saying 'Similia similibus curantus' (i.e. like is cured by like).

The dilute forms that are used are called *potencies*. In itself, this is of course rather strange. The word potency means 'force'. Now, it would seem obvious that a particular substance will lose much of its potency if we dilute it. Yet, however, this does not seem to be the case. By diluting a substance in the correct way, more and more of its 'force' is released. In practice, this means that the greater the dilution, the further the substance penetrates into our body.

Dilutions are indicated by the capital letter D. This means a decimal dilution. We find, for example, D1, D2, up to D200. D1 means 1:10. D2 = 1:100, etc. Up to D12 we speak of low potencies. D12 to D30 are medium potencies.

Above that, we speak of high potencies. For acute illness, low potencies are generally used. Chronic ailments are dealt with by the higher potencies. It is also sometimes claimed that the lower potencies have more effect on the physical body and the higher more on the mental side.

The following homoeopathic remedies may be considered for our kidneys, eyes and skin: *Apis, Kalium arsenicum, Natrium sulfuricum, Lycopodium, Arnica, Chamomilla, Argentum nitricum, Cineraria maritima,* Sulphur and *Acidum nitricum.*

Apis
This is the homoeopathically dilute bee toxin. It is used for acute inflammation of the kidneys, where the following symptoms occur: oedematic swelling, urine deficiency, acute sleepiness and lack of thirst. It is used in low potencies. Five drops four times a day. In cases of high fever, *Belladonna* or *Aconitum* can also be used in addition to this remedy.

Kalium Arsenicum
This substance is useful for chronic inflammation of the kidneys. A few symptoms are advanced emaciation, dry and toneless skin, breathlessness and dropsical swelling of the legs, anxiety states affecting the facial expression, dissatisfaction and repeated complaints about all kinds of trivia, and chronic eczema which irritates when near heat.

The remedy can be used in potencies of 3 and 4. Five grains three times dailys is adequate. Complement this homoeopathic approach with a good herbal tea and, above all, investigate the cause!

Natrium sulfuricum

In addition to the remedies already referred to,
Natrium sulfuricum can be used for kidney
stone. An important characteristic of this
substance is that complaints become worse in
damp weather. Kidney stone patients must
therefore preferably not live in a damp house!
Natrium sulfuricum is used in a potency of six.
Three grains four times a day, to be taken
fifteen minutes before meals.

Lycopodium

This substance (Stagshorn Clubmoss) was dealt
with in detail when the various herbs were
discussed. It should be used in a potency of
thirty when the condition described occurs.
Five grains once a week is sufficient.

Lycopodium may be used in potencies of six
and twelve to prevent the formation of new
kidney stones. The effect of this substance is not
only an ego strengthening one, but it stimulates
the whole metabolism. We commonly see that
disturbance of the liver function may lead to
kidney stones. 'According to Dr Voorhoeve,
Lycopodium is especially effective in cases of
uratic stones.

Arnica

This substance can be taken internally for
kidney bleeding. It is then taken in potencies of
four and six. If we wish to harmonize a tense
situation, it should preferably be taken in
potencies of thirty or even 200. This remedy was
dealt with in detail when the herbs were
discussed. At D30, five grains are taken once
every two weeks. If *Arnica* is taken in D200, five
grains once every two or three months will
suffice.

Chamomilla

As a support for other herbs or homoeopathic remedies (the more organically aligned remedies) use may be made of *Chamomilla* D6 to D12. This dilution of Camomile tincture is particularly soothing on our spiritual life. Greater detail will be found about this in Chapter 4, where the Camomile was discussed.

Argentum nitricum

This substance is one of the most important eye remedies that exists. *Argentum* is homoeopathically diluted silver. It is very successfully applied to eye inflammations accompanied with discharge. Dependent on the type of constitution, D6 or D30 may be used. With D6, five grains three times daily, with D30, five grains once a week will suffice.

I shall mention only one point about it here. Silver is analogous to the cosmic pattern represented by the moon. The moon indicates the reflective powers of man, his ability to react. For example, we apply silver to the back of a piece of glass to produce a mirror. Looking in the mirror is in fact nothing other than reflecting ourselves.

As already stated, the eyes are the *mirrors* of the soul. We use our eyes to reflect the mood of our emotional life. If we examine all this we shall discover that all the aspects referred to (eyes, silver, reflection, moon, reactive powers, etc.) are analogous to each other.

Cineraria maritima

In his book *Homoeopathy in Practice*, Dr Voorhoeve writes as follows about this substance. 'The *Cineraria maritima*, which is native to the Near East, is a traditional remedy for cataract. Nowadays, it is marketed in the

form of eye drops under the name 'Cineralyt'
(By Messrs. Madaus of Cologne). 'One drop is
dropped into the outer corner of the eye once a
day, the eye is closed and the liquid is carefully
rubbed towards the opposite corner. To begin
with, there might be a slight feeling of smarting,
which proves that the eye is reacting favourably
to the treatment. A week should be left after a
period of daily treatment.'

I felt that I had to insert this quotation after
seeing the results that have been achieved with
this natural remedy.

Sulphur
This is one of the most important homoeopathic
substances. It has so many different actions that
a large book could easily be written on this
subject alone.

To some extent, it is a pity that it has to be
included under this heading since the scope of
this book does not allow the background of this
remedy to be investigated further. On the other
hand, the specific is too important to be left out.

Now, there are people who display a
tendency to attract everything impure to
themselves (this refers chiefly to spiritual
impurity) not consciously, but due to their own
life pattern. The 'sulphur' person lives very
impurely and knows no true joy in life. This
inward impurity must be worked out of the
body. The eyes and the skin are the places
where this happens. If eczema, certain forms of
acne and ailments of the eye are paired with the
following psychic symptoms, sulphur should
immediately be considered as a valuable
curative.

Psychic symptoms associated with 'sulphur
complaints'. People who are ego-centric and
take little account of others, who have little

interest in material affairs, who are very
forgetful, who have great difficulty in reflection,
who entertain all kinds of illusions, who are
quickly irritated, quickly depressed, and
sometimes rather suspicious. Despite good
food, they remain rather weak and on the lean
side. As soon as these symptoms, i.e. both
physical and spiritual, are diagnosed as present,
it is worth taking sulphur in a potency of D6.
Five grains three times daily, half an hour before
meal times.

Acidum nitricum

For certain physical symptoms, we can think of
causes that are not the true ones. This is the
case, for example, with *fissures* and *breaks* in
the skin. Often, we blame this on work that we
have done with our hands, if the fissures appear
in the hands, or to straining at stool if the
fissures becomes noticeable round the anus,
etc. The true background will be clear to you if
you understood something of the first chapters
of this book.

Fissures are the body's emergency measures.
They are due to cumulations of feelings that
have become so strong that they have been
expelled via an open break in the skin. It is
therefore, in principle, wrong to close up a
break in the skin with all kinds of ointments. In
doing so, you again close up what the body has
itself created as a way out. It is much better to
combat such disorders of the skin with a good
kidney tea (*Solidago, Ononis,* etc.) in order to
stimulate the kidneys to greater activity. The
blood is then cleansed by the kidneys and, as far
as purification is concerned, need seek no way
out through the skin.

Where fissures are painful, deep and
ulcerous, *Acidum nitricum* in a potency of D4

appears to do good service. Five grains or drops three times daily is adequate.

The above substances can be obtained from a homoeopathic pharmacist. In all cases you would do better to visit an expert than to keep messing about yourself with a specific complaint without it improving. You can, however, apply the remedies mentioned in this chapter yourself without difficulty. If no improvement takes place in the course of time, an expert can always still be consulted. A list of doctors who practice homoeopathy in the United Kingdom can be obtained from the Faculty of Homoeopathy, The Royal London Homoeopathic Hospital, Great Ormond Street, London WC1.

CHAPTER SIX

OUR DAILY FOOD AS A CURATIVE

The world in which we live is a bundle of contradictions. We can find examples of this in many quarters. We shall take a brief look at one of these contradictions. It might best be described as follows: on the one hand, science is becoming increasingly convinced of the essential part that the food we eat plays in the matter of our sickness and health; but on the other hand, this same science stops at nothing in order to develop products which quite simply constitute an assault on our health.

It has, in fact, gradually come down to a real struggle when we realize all the kinds of things that we can buy by way of foodstuffs. In the past, people tended to speak of 'victuals'. You will find little mention of this word in the present day. We now talk about 'foodstuffs'. This is quite correct up to a certain point, and points to the fact that science is at least honest, even if probably unconsciously. We must realize that foodstuffs are not necessarily victuals.

Many foodstuffs ensure that our taste requirements are satisfied and that our hunger is stilled. A victual ensures that the substances needed for our physical and spiritual health are supplied. This is something fundamentally different. Unfortunately, we live at a time when people are becoming more and more careless with their food. Our social pattern is partly the cause of this. Tins, jars and instant meals are the order of the day. For many people, this is the sole remaining criteria. As soon as we recognize that a large percentage of physical ailments can be attributed to eating quite valueless and even harmful food, we can again start looking at our daily food as a curative.

In many cases, physical ailments seem to disappear when we adopt a healthy diet (which is nothing other than *normal* healthy food), but the ailments will reappear as soon as we return to the refined and processed foods we so commonly use. There are people who try and compensate for their spiritual poverty by eating delicacies, drinking and 'being merry'. Now, there is nothing against being merry, provided it originates from a true feeling of joy in the fine things that we experience. Alas, many people become merry only under the influence of disharmonious expression of human thought.

Here are a few pointers to sound nourishment:

Always eat more base-producers than acid producers
Base-producers are (preferably raw) vegetables and fruit. Acid-producers are albuminous products, chiefly animal albumina. Carbohydrate foodstuffs form both acids and bases.

Eat as little preserved foodstuffs as possible
Whatever the method of preservation adopted, the quality of the food suffers greatly. Vitamins especially will have been affected. In many cases, preservatives and artificial flavours will have been added. Despite checks on this, I nevertheless feel that unnatural and toxic substances cannot but be harmful to the body.

Under all circumstances, use only wholemeal cereals
Pigs are often better off than people. Pig feed in

fact contains the bran (which contains the most valuable components of the grain) rejected by man because white bread, after all, looks more 'civilized' than coarse brown bread. All food prepared from denatured meal is ballast to our bodies.

Eat as little sugar and other luxuries as possible

Sugar produces yeast in the bowels and can destroy the valuable elements in our food. If you cannot control your intake of sugar, then buy cane sugar. This is less harmful than the intake of white, refined sugar. Honey is a wholesome food and can fully satisfy our need for sugar. A teaspoon of honey in your tea tastes better than sugar.

Always take something fatty in the meals

Fat in this context means vegetable oil, preferably cold-pressed. It substantially improves digestion.

Eat only when you are hungry

Being really hungry is something we no longer experience (unfortunately). We spend the best part of the day satisfying our taste with all kinds of bits and pieces (what we call 'snacks'). After a meal, our digestive system needs rest in order to allow your mind to process the impressions it has received. Allow your stomach some peace!

As far as the subject of this book is concerned, we might add the following. If you have trouble with your 'feeling organs', make sure that not much salt is taken. Salt stimulates our mental life. Through the excess in feeling, our minds are already active enough, so that further stimulation by taking salt will not be gratefully accepted. However, take just a little salt each day, not refined kitchen salt, but coarse sea-salt.

Eat a good deal of raw food especially fruit. This promotes the detoxification of the body. Nourishment for the kidney, skin or eye patient must be fully aimed at *cleansing*. In this way, the organs that have to cope with the excess of 'spiritual poison' become unburdened and are thereby given an opportunity to recuperate through rest.

CHAPTER SEVEN

A VADE-MECUM AND CONCLUSION

The thoughts on which this book is based really conflict with the intention of a vade-mecum. A vade-mecum is generally used as a kind of 'hand-to-mouth' word list. Headache? ... this pill; sore throat? ... a different remedy. In such cases, it is not a question of curing but of eliminating annoying symptoms. If lasting results are to be achieved, resolute action on both the physical and the mental causes is absolutely necessary.

The following vade-mecum is no more than a systematic .summary of the various forms of affectations of our 'feeling organs' with the related remedies. Before actually proceeding to take a specific herb or other remedy, you would do well first to read what has been written about it in the preceding section.

In this way, you can find out whether the herb concerned is entirely analogous to your case. Using the vade-mecum in this way therapy can be aligned to the overall situation and the remedy will not be used merely to eliminate a symptom.

Finally, I must stress the seriousness of the disorders discussed in this book. Never, therefore, go to a 'quack'. If you do not know enough about unofficial medicine, there is fortunately enough opportunity for consulting experts.

Never compare the natural approach to medicine with the allopathic. Do not polarize them but try and combine. Your allopathic doctor may possibly have some objection if you tell him what you are concerned with. This must not prevent you from putting your cards on the table. As soon as he sees that you yourself are co-operating in the healing process, especially by trying to tackle the true background, he cannot but be pleased. Perhaps, as a result, he may even come to value the natural way of medicine.

KIDNEY AILMENTS

Sluggish kidneys	Golden Rod, *Ononis,* Celery, Parsley, *Arnica,* Stagshorn Clubmoss
Inflammation of the kidneys and bladder	*Apis,* Golden Rod, *Ononis,* Camomile
Stone in the kidney and bladder	*Rubia, Natrium sulfuricum,* Golden Rod, *Ononis ,* Celery, Blackthorn
Kidney bleeding (e.g. as a result of stone)	*Arnica, Tormentilla* and Blackthorn
To prevent new formation of stone	*Rubia, Lycopodium*
Dropsical swelling as the result of sluggish kidney function	*Ononis,* Poplar
Accumulation of fluid in the legs	Lime blossom or leaf

EYE AILMENTS

Inflamed eyes	Eyebright, Camomile, *Argentum nitricum*
Reduced powers of sight	Fresh Carrot juice, *Argentum metallicum, Arnica*
Cataract	*Cineraria maritima*

SKIN AILMENTS

Eczema and acne	Golden Rod, *Kalium arsenicum*, Sulphur, Stinging Nettle, St John's Wort
Fissures in the skin	*Acidum nitricum*
Adolescent spots	Stinging Nettle, Sulphur
To support many remedies, the spirit can be 'comforted' with	Balm, Camomile

The following is a summary of the herbs dealt with in this book and covers location, flowering period, picking period and parts used.

GOLDEN ROD
A perennial that can exceed a yard in height. The stem is reddish in colour and angled. Smooth. The yellow flowers form small ears.
Flowering period: July to September.
Picking period: July and August.
Parts used: the upper tips (including the flowers).

REST HARROW
Perennial growing from one to two feet. The ends of the twiglets form thorns. The flowers are a fine pink. The plant has an unpleasant smell.
Flowering period: June to September.
Picking period: in the autumn and during flowering.
Parts used: the root and the dried herb (stalk, leaves and flowers).

STINGING NETTLE
A well known weed. Two varieties occur: the small and the large stinging nettle. The small

nettle appears to be more effective than the large.
Flowering period: March to September.
Picking period: during flowering.
Parts used: the whole herb.

CAMOMILE
An annual with flowers with a golden-yellow centre with radiating petals.
Flowering period: June and July.
Picking period: July.
Parts used: the dried flowers.

CELERY
A well known garden herb. Only the leaf and stalks are used. It can be used throughout the growing season.

PARSLEY
(as for celery)

EYEBRIGHT
An annual with stemless white flowers. The plant has 'box' fruit.
Flowering period: from June to September.
Picking period: July and August.
Parts used: flowers, leaves and stalks.

ARNICA
A perennial whose leaves form a 'root rosette'. The stalk grows from this rosette. The flowers are a fine orange in colour.
Flowering period: June and July.
Picking period: throughout the flowering period.
Parts used: the flowers and leaves (the root is also used in homoeopathy).

STAGSHORN CLUBMOSS
A creeping plant. The stalk ends in a thin ear containing powder.
Flowering period: July and August.
Picking period: July.
Parts used: the whole herb.

BLACKTHORN
A tapering, bushy plant. White flowers. The fruit is about one centimetre in diameter and is blue-black in colour.
Flowering period: April and May.
Picking period: throughout flowering.
Parts used: flowers and leaves.

LIME BLOSSOM
The blossom is the part of the lime tree used. It can be picked in April and May.

BALM
A herbaceous plant growing from two to three feet. White flowers. It has a strong lemon scent.
Flowering period: July and August.
Picking period: before flowering.
Parts used: leaf and stalk.

When collecting herbs yourself, plan your picking and have respect for nature. Do not destroy unnecessarily but proceed sparingly. Enjoy to the full the goodness that the Creator has entrusted to us!